NAT
STU

by
Martyn Bramwell

Piccolo
A Piper Book

Contents

Introduction

No other hobby or pastime has quite as much variety and fascination as exploring the world of nature.

That world begins right outside your own back door, whether you live in the country, in a small town, or even in the middle of a big industrial city. And, best of all, it is there for you to explore all through the year. Spring, summer, autumn and winter, plant and animal life always has something new and different to offer. The world of nature is like a living kaleidoscope, and one of the greatest rewards of all is to understand how hundreds of very different plants, insects, birds and mammals all fit together in a perfectly balanced system.

Something for everyone

Nature study has almost as many different aspects as nature itself. Which one you choose will depend on your own particular interests. You may enjoy the detective work of piecing together the patterns of life in a small living community, such as a single tree, a pond, or a corner of the garden. You may develop a special interest in the fieldcraft skills of watching birds or mammals in their natural surroundings. Some people are most intrigued by the biology of *how* things work in nature. Others are fascinated by the way animals behave – by *what* they do, *when* they do it, and, most of all, *why*. Whichever path you choose, this book will help you off to a good start.

The experimental approach

For those who like the scientific approach, this book is packed with ideas and projects. No expensive special equipment is required; just an enquiring mind, some imagination – and sometimes a bit of patience. As long as you take care not to cause any unnecessary suffering to insects and other small animals, and avoid picking rare plants – or indeed any that are growing on their own or in very small groups – your collecting and experimenting will not cause any harm to the natural world.

Finally, whether you are exploring a wood or a riverbank, or using sharp blades or hot liquids in a home experiment, remember that SAFETY COMES FIRST.

1: Nature Watch

To get the best out of watching wildlife you will need to combine the stealth and cunning of a hunter with plenty of patience and the eyes and ears of a scientific observer. But you will find the rewards are well worth the effort.

Imagine watching young birds making their first attempts to fly; or a hedgehog shuffling along in search of his evening meal; or the magic moment when a brilliantly-coloured dragonfly shrugs off the last of its larval skin, spreads out its wings to dry, and then darts off into the sunshine to hunt. These and other sights are not difficult to see if you know when, where and how to look for them.

You can explore the natural world wherever you are, but the best place to start is close to home. Begin by making a general survey, on foot or by bicycle, to discover all the most likely places for wildlife studies. Look for old hedgerows, patches of woodland, rivers, small streams and ponds. Even in large towns there are often small woods and other bits of countryside, as well as parks, playing fields and ornamental gardens offering food, shelter and living space to a huge variety of animal life.

What to wear

How you dress will depend on the time of year and the weather, but the general rule is to make sure you are always warm, dry and comfortable. Basic outdoor clothes should include strong boots or walking shoes, thick socks, a warm shirt and at least one sweater, and an anorak with plenty of pockets. You will also need a back-pack to hold your notebooks, specimen containers and – if you are going out for most of the day – some food and a flask of hot drink. Remember that weather conditions can change quite quickly, especially in hill country, and that a blazing hot afternoon can easily give way to a very cool evening – just about the time you might want to sit perfectly still for an hour or so to watch some interesting animal behaviour. At times like this, an experienced observer reaches into the pack for an extra sweater and a woollen hat, and settles down to watch in comfort.

Special equipment

Very little special equipment is necessary, but you *will* need a

▼ See how many different kinds of moss, lichen and fungus, and how many different insects and grubs, inhabit an old stump.

notebook and pencils if you are going to keep a record of your finds. You will also need some containers if you plan to collect specimens. A few sheets of newspaper will be useful for wrapping pieces of bark, twigs and other fairly strong specimens. For small, delicate objects like insects, bird **pellets**, flowers and thin shells, take an assortment of plastic bottles and boxes. Plastic tablet tubes plugged with cotton wool are particularly useful for small insects.

One item you probably *will* want to buy is a good hand-lens. Large magnifying glasses are easy to use, but remember to keep the lens in a cloth bag to protect it from scratches. If you are planning to do a lot of field work, choose one of the small folding lenses with a magnification of about ×10. To use this type, first hold the lens close to the eye (about 2–3 cm away) then slowly bring the specimen into focus by moving it towards you with the other hand.

Make your own 'pooter'

This curiously-named piece of equipment will enable you to collect tiny insects without damaging them. You will need a wide-necked jar with a tight-fitting rubber stopper, bored to take two lengths of right-angled glass or rigid plastic tubing, a longer piece of rubber tube and a small piece of fine gauze. (You can get these items from large chemists, or from shops selling wine-making equipment.) Assemble the pooter as shown in the drawing. To collect a specimen, simply place the open end of the short tube close to the insect and suck through the rubber mouthpiece. The insect is immediately sucked into the jar – and the gauze makes it quite impossible for you to swallow your catch!

Use a slightly dampened paint-brush to transfer the specimen from the pooter to a temporary storage container. Usually you will only keep the insect long enough to identify it, sketch it and make your field notes. It should then be released – as close as possible to where it was caught.

However, if you decide to build up a permanent collection of larger insects, such as beetles, butterflies or moths, you will have to learn to use various chemicals for killing the specimens painlessly and for relaxing and preserving them. You will also want to learn how to mount the insects for display. Most of the chemicals can be ordered only from specialist

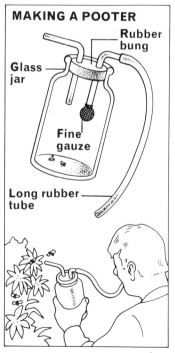

MAKING A POOTER

Rubber bung

Glass jar

Fine gauze

Long rubber tube

suppliers, and the best way of obtaining them, and of learning how to use them properly is by joining a naturalists' club.

The naturalist's notebook

If you make careful notes and sketches of your observations, as shown at the bottom of this page, you will quickly build up a large store of information which you can refer back to at any time.

Start each entry on a fresh page, with a record of the date, weather conditions, and exactly where you are. That way you can easily return to the same spot if, for example, you want to collect seeds from a wild flower later in the year, or take a close look at a nest once the young birds have left.

When you have filled several books it is very useful to make a subject index in another book. Then, if you want to collect butterfly eggs or caterpillars for an experiment like that on page 47, you simply look up 'Butterflies' in the index and find the list of all your butterfly observations – 'Holly Blue, book 2, page 7', etc.

Leaves damaged by leaf-cutter bees

Two-spot ladybird

Aphids on stem

Tracks and other animal signs

In any **habitat**, there is always a chance that you will catch sight of some local wildlife. But usually this will be little more than a fleeting glimpse as the animal dashes into cover.

To get in really close, and have time to watch the animals behaving naturally, needs much more careful planning. First of all you need to find out which animals are living in the area, so spend some time walking slowly and quietly through the habitat looking for clues.

The most obvious signs are footprints, so look carefully wherever there is bare earth, especially by the banks of streams or ponds where animals might come to drink. On beaches, look for bird prints in the firm damp sand just above the water-line, especially where there are worm casts or other signs of burrowing creatures that seabirds feed on. Fresh snowfalls in winter offer a marvellous chance to look for tracks, especially in farming areas with a landscape of fields, hedgerows and woodland. With luck you might find the tracks of deer, rabbits, foxes, voles, hedgehogs and other animals, linking their burrows and dens to their feeding areas.

In addition to footprints, animals leave many other signs. Nuts, fruits, berries and

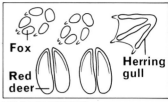

FOOTPRINTS

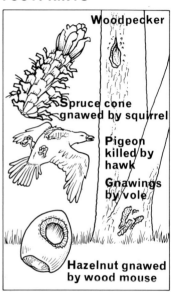

Woodpecker

Spruce cone gnawed by squirrel

Pigeon killed by hawk

Gnawings by vole

Hazelnut gnawed by wood mouse

FEEDING SIGNS

pine cones often bear teeth-marks that clearly identify the animal that fed on them. Plant stems may show signs of nibbling by voles, and young trees may have their bark stripped off by a number of different animals, especially in winter when food supplies run short.

Some animals use a regular route from one part of their territory to another. Rabbits,

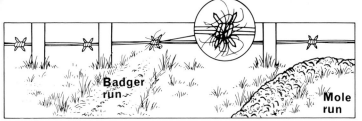

REGULAR TRAILS

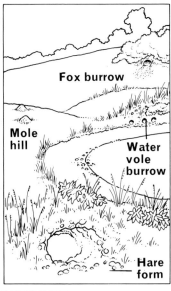

BURROWS

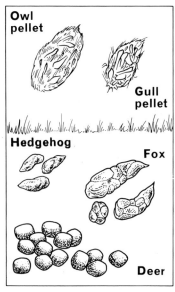

PELLETS AND DROPPINGS

hares and deer often beat paths across ploughed fields, moles leave unmistakable runs and mounds above their tunnels, while badgers and foxes also have their regular routes. Keep an eye on holes in hedges and scrapes underneath barbed wire fences. Tell-tale wisps of hair caught on barbs or twigs may also reveal who has passed that way recently.

Many hunting and scavenging birds 'cough up' pellets made of bits of bone, fur or other indigestible bits of the food they have eaten. These, too, are useful clues: look for them beneath trees and at the foot of tall fence-posts or telegraph poles where the birds may perch.

There are many more clues to look for and we can show only a

few examples here. If you want to know more there are several specialized guide books on the subject. And as well as revealing which animals live where, many of these clues can be used to form the basis of fascinating collections and displays.

Fieldcraft skills

Animals take fright at anything that appears to be a threat, so the first rule of fieldcraft is to keep quiet, move slowly and steadily, and blend into the scenery as much as possible.

Dull brown, grey and green clothing is suitable for most habitats. (Brightly-coloured waterproof coveralls will help you keep track of each other if the weather turns nasty, but keep them in the back-pack until needed.)

Most animals have very sharp hearing, so noise will be one of your main enemies. If you are with a friend, use simple hand signals for 'Come on', 'Stop', 'Get down' and so on. And if you do need to talk, do it quietly. One loud call can clear every animal in the area. When moving, use the 'cover' of natural sounds. On a beach, or among sand dunes, crawl forward as each wave breaks, then pause. In open woodland, long grass or reed-beds, move each time the wind rustles the vegetation.

Even more important than sound is scent. A fox will smell you coming half a kilometre away if the wind is carrying your scent towards him. And in highland country, grazing red deer will be on the alert at several times that range. So, whatever the habitat, always approach from down-wind so that the animal's scent is carried towards you and not the other way round. This is why it is such an advantage to know your local area really well. Then, no matter what the wind direction, you will always be able to plan a safe approach to any spot you want to visit. If you decide to look for foxes or badgers at dusk, get there early and find a safe place a few metres up a tree, so that any breeze will carry your scent over the animal's head.

The *way* you move is also very important. Avoid sudden movements – they spell danger to animals, and birds in particular are easy to frighten. If an animal looks towards you or appears uneasy, keep quite still until it relaxes and carries on with what it was doing. If a flock of birds or a group of rabbits takes fright, just sit tight; they will soon return and continue feeding if you do not pose a threat.

Finally, always try to hide your shape. Instead of sitting out in the open, sit with your back against a tree or a hedge. On a beach, sit by a breakwater or amongst the debris at high-water. On a hillside, choose a place amongst exposed rocks or in a patch of bracken or heather. Most important of all, try to avoid breaking the skyline. Suddenly poking your head and shoulders above a wall or hedge will terrify any animal on the other side. Peep round the edge of a gateway, or look for a gap to look through like the observer in the drawing on page 6. Use the same approach when you reach the brow of a hill or when you climb out of a stream gulley. It is usually best to lie down, crawl slowly to the top, and peep through the grass before standing up.

Baits and other lures

Once you are familiar with the wildlife in your area, and especially once you know the location of animals' burrows and some of their regular tracks, you can use other techniques to make observing them even easier.

One way is to put down bait to encourage them to remain in one place while you watch from a nearby hiding place. Remember that small animals are very nervous if they feel exposed, so place the bait just at the edge of a track, close to cover. For squirrels and field-mice try a mixture of suet, raisins and oatmeal. Bank voles are often attracted to chopped carrot and cereals. Rabbits go for carrots, lettuces and apples, while the small hunters, like stoats and weasels, may be lured by pieces of fish, or offal from a butcher's shop. Place a small amount of bait in a likely spot, and check next day to see if it was taken. Repeat this for a few days and then choose a fine evening, get in position early, and wait. A useful observer's aid can be made by covering a flashlight lens with red cellophane film. The red light will improve your view without alarming the animal (see below).

Baiting works best in autumn and winter when normal food

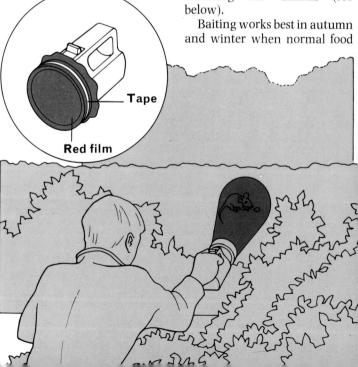

Tape

Red film

supplies are less plentiful. A hungry animal is less likely to be put off by any slight traces of your scent left on the bait.

Moths and other night-flying insects can be attracted by a baiting technique known as 'sugaring'. Mix together equal quantities of beer, black treacle and rum, and paint the sweet liquid onto fence posts or tree trunks close to a good moth habitat, such as a thick hedge or the edge of a wood. You will soon have a huge variety of insect life to study. Another very effective method is to shine a powerful torch onto a white sheet draped over a bush or hung from a branch. Insects will quickly settle all over the sheet and you can examine them at your leisure.

Nature's grave-diggers

As soon as a plant or animal dies, the process of **recycling** begins. You can make a study of this as a special project. If you find a dead bird or small mammal, pin it down under some wire mesh near a hedge-bottom or other insect-rich habitat. Then visit the site regularly and make notes on the insect visitors and their activities. Blowflies will lay their eggs so that the maggots can feed on the body. Ground beetles and rove beetles will come to prey on the maggots, and burying beetles and sexton beetles will dig away beneath the body until they have buried it in a shallow grave – a food store for their own grubs, which are laid in nearby tunnels.

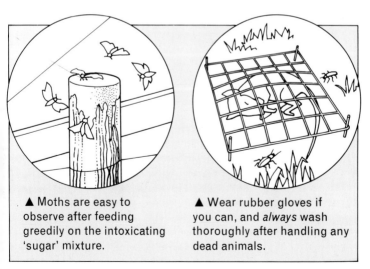

▲ Moths are easy to observe after feeding greedily on the intoxicating 'sugar' mixture.

▲ Wear rubber gloves if you can, and *always* wash thoroughly after handling any dead animals.

2: Habitat Studies

No matter how fascinating an individual animal or plant may be, it is just one small part of a much bigger and even more fascinating biological jig-saw puzzle involving dozens of other plants and animals.

In any habitat, or 'living space', there are all sorts of specialists, but they occupy clearly defined levels in the system. First there are the plants, which use the energy of the sun to create living tissue. Next come the **herbivores** (plant eaters), ranging in size from microbes and tiny sap-sucking insects, through rabbits and deer to elephants and giraffes. Above them come the hunting **carnivores** (meat-eaters) – spiders, shrews, foxes and cats. And right at the top of the pyramid sit the greatest hunters of all – the eagles, the big cats of the jungle, sharks and killer whales.

Large-scale habitats include oceans, deserts, tropical forests and grasslands. But there are many smaller units that also form distinct habitats – hedgerows, small ponds, moorlands and river estuaries. The fascination lies in working out which animals and plants live there, how each one has specialized in living in that habitat, and how they relate to their neighbours.

Habitat survey methods

A good starting point is to make a detailed survey of a small habitat such as a grassy bank between a hedgerow and a country road. In addition to your notebook and a couple of good identification guides to wild flowers and grasses, you will need a simple piece of equipment called a quadrat. This is a wooden frame, one metre along each side, divided into 10 cm squares by lengths of string or wire (see above).

To guarantee a random sample, drop the quadrat over your shoulder, as shown in the inset above, then try to identify the plants in each square. Make a copy of the grid squares in your notebook and draw in the plants. Repeat the experiment at various places along the bank and you will be able to build up a picture of the natural plant-mixture – the 'flora' of the bank.

The illustration also shows young naturalists surveying a 30-metre sample section of an old hedge. They are describing, sketching and measuring all the different plants. As long as the sample section is well away from woodland (a source of other types of plant seeds, not typical of natural hedgerows) you can use this kind of survey to estimate the age of a hedge. Count all the shrub and tree species, plus wild roses, but ignore seedlings and also climbers like brambles and honeysuckle. A hedge made up of three kinds of shrub plant and two tree species will be about 500 years old – one century for each of the main plant members.

Exploring the underworld

The third activity in the main illustration shows samples being taken of the soil, and also of the **leaf-litter** – the thin layer of dead plant material lying on the ground.

At first glance this layer might look uninteresting; but look closely. It is full of animal life, because this is where the serious business of recycling really begins. Vast numbers of highly specialized insects (and millions of other organisms too small to see) chew their way through the litter. They take what they need, and break down the litter physically and chemically so that carbon, nitrogen and other essential elements are returned to the soil for use by growing plants. Even here, there are the hunters and the hunted. Spiders, rove beetles and centipedes prey on the plant-eaters – and are in turn preyed upon by hedge sparrows, shrews and hedgehogs.

Collecting your samples

Plastic boxes with snap-on lids (such as those in which ice-cream and margarine are sold) are ideal for leaf-litter samples. Simply scrape the litter into the box, making sure your sample goes right down to the soil level. Soil samples can be taken using a small gardening trowel. Alternatively, in soft soil, you can use a tin – for example a ground coffee tin with a plastic snap-on lid. The tin is simply pressed into the ground, then rocked and twisted so that it can be lifted free. The top should be put back immediately.

Extracting the soil-dwellers

As a first stage, put the sample through a coarse sieve (about 1 cm mesh) to remove bits of twig, leaf, small stones and any

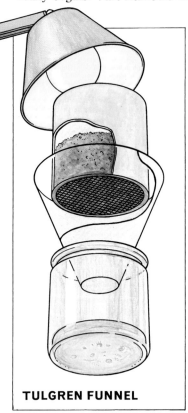

TULGREN FUNNEL

large animals such as snails, worms and centipedes.

To extract the smaller soil animals you will have to make an apparatus called a Tulgren Funnel (left). The soil container is a food tin with both ends removed, and wire gauze with a 2–5 mm mesh glued over the lower end. Use a metal funnel, or make one from smooth, stiff card, and fit a 25-watt bulb to an ordinary desk light for the heat source. The three parts can be stacked one inside the other as shown, or, for greater stability, you could support them with stiff wire loops fixed to a simple upright wooden frame.

Part-fill the soil container, switch on the lamp and leave it on for a few hours. The soil animals are used to dark, cold, damp conditions, so they will move away from the heat source, pass through the gauze, and slip down the funnel into the collecting jar. The animals will die very quickly in warm dry conditions, so empty the jar at regular intervals, and while you are examining them and sorting them, place them in a plastic box as shown above, with some damp blotting paper in the bottom. You can use the dampened tip of a paintbrush to move the animals about. Unwanted specimens can be released into a cool damp part of the garden, while specimens needed for a permanent collection are humanely killed (see page 8) and then transferred into small, tightly-stopped glass or plastic containers partly

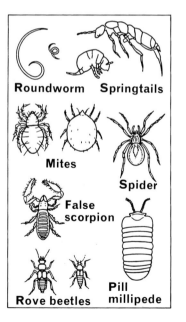

Roundworm   Springtails

Mites

Spider

False scorpion

Rove beetles   Pill millipede

filled with preserving solution. The alcohol used by laboratories and museums may not be sold for hobby use, but dispensing chemists can usually supply formaldehyde in the form of a 5% solution and this is ideal for most small specimens. THIS CHEMICAL IS AN IRRITANT, SO AVOID INHALING ANY VAPOUR AND WASH YOUR HANDS THOROUGHLY AFTER USING THE SOLUTION.

Make sure you label each of your specimen tubes carefully, giving the name of the insect, the date, and a note of where you collected it. You can extend this project by comparing the soil and litter communities of different habitats, such as an oak-beech forest, a pine forest, a high moor and a riverside meadow.

The hidden life of an oak

You can build an entire project around the huge variety of animal life to be found in a single tree. And one of the best subjects of all is a solitary oak growing in an old hedgerow.

By taking photographs at different times of the year, observing the resident and visiting birds, and collecting samples of the leaves, twigs and fruits, and the ever-changing insect population, you can build up an illustrated diary of the tree's annual cycle of life.

The caterpillars of moths and butterflies feed on the leaves, while other insects and their larvae bore tunnels inside the leaves. Oak aphids suck the sap – and in turn are preyed on by ladybirds and lacewings. Scores of different insects, including tiny wasps, mites, aphids and sawflies lay their eggs in the leaves, and the leaves react by producing **galls** of many shapes and colours (see pages 44–45).

One simple way of collecting insects is to lay an old sheet on the ground beneath the tree and beat or shake the lower branches. Your catch will usually contain several kinds of weevil, easily identified by their odd 'long-nosed' appearance, and other beetles such as longhorns, cockchafers and the impressive stag beetles.

If you find loose pieces of bark on the trunk or branches, gently lift them up. Underneath, you may find the intricate patterns of tunnels bored by the oak bark beetle. If the bark is completely loose, take it for your collection, otherwise ease it back into place.

Finally, don't forget to investigate the soil beneath the tree. Here you are likely to find wire-worms, cockchafer beetle larvae, tiny burrowing wasps, and perhaps even the evil-looking larvae of the tiger beetle lurking just below the surface.

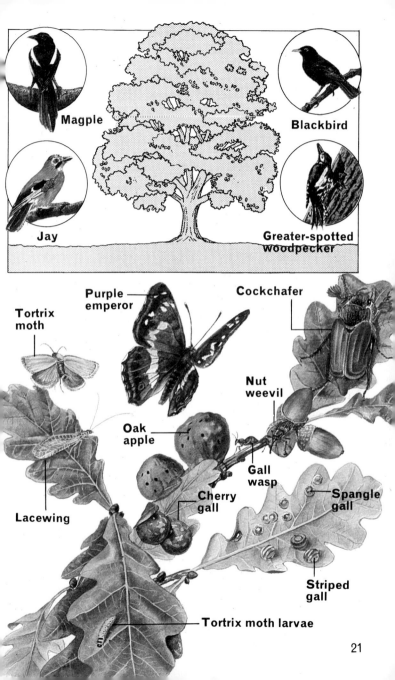

Magpie

Blackbird

Jay

Greater-spotted
woodpecker

Tortrix
moth

Purple
emperor

Cockchafer

Nut
weevil

Oak
apple

Gall
wasp

Cherry
gall

Spangle
gall

Lacewing

Striped
gall

Tortrix moth larvae

21

Investigating pond life

Exploring the life of ponds and streams can be great fun, but remember to TAKE EXTRA CARE. Never go exploring this kind of habitat alone, and don't allow enthusiasm to lead you into taking any risks.

For these investigations, two extra pieces of equipment will be useful – and both are simple and cheap to make. The first is a viewing tube. All you do is cut both ends off a fairly large tin and cover one end with clear polythene or kitchen film. Place the covered end in the water and look down the tube. The viewer cuts out the distortion caused by surface ripples, and also avoids the dazzling effect of light reflected off the water.

The second item is a sampling net made from very fine-meshed netting (the end of an old stocking will do). The open top end is supported by a wire frame attached to a bamboo pole, while the bottom end is firmly tied round the neck of a

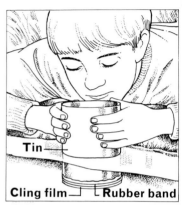

Tin

Cling film ⌐ ⌐ Rubber band

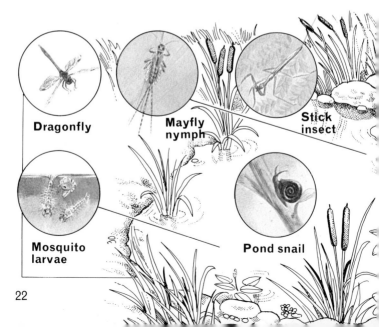

Dragonfly

Mayfly nymph

Stick insect

Mosquito larvae

Pond snail

small plastic bottle. Used with a gentle sweeping motion, the net is a good way of collecting tiny aquatic organisms.

Where to look

There are four main living areas in the pond habitat. First, look out for pond skaters and whirligig beetles walking on the surface film of the water, and then for the larvae of mosquitoes and other insects hanging beneath the film with their breathing tubes just breaking the surface.

Next, use your sampling net to explore the mid-waters for tadpoles, sticklebacks, diving beetles and tiny water fleas and mites. Pond snails, leeches, stick insects and the nymphs of dragonflies cling to the stems of water weeds. Finally, use a jam-jar tied to a long string to dredge samples of mud from the bottom. Here you should find more nymphs and larvae, tiny water scorpions and maybe small freshwater mussels.

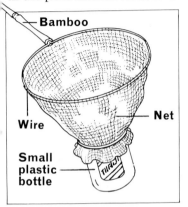

— **Bamboo**

Wire

Net

Small plastic bottle

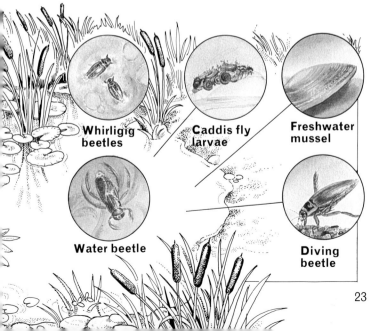

Whirligig beetles

Caddis fly larvae

Freshwater mussel

Water beetle

Diving beetle

Life on the seashore

The seashore is a fascinating and complex habitat. Here, dry land meets water, and fresh-water rivers mix with salt sea waters. The land itself varies from fine sticky mud, through sand and shingle to bare rock, and many animals have to cope with being underwater for part of each day, and exposed to wind and sun for the rest.

To avoid being dried up and killed by the sun when the tide goes out, limpets clamp themselves tightly against the rocks, trapping life-saving moisture inside their shells. Barnacles do much the same thing, closing the movable openings in their shells, then opening them to

extend their feeding tentacles when the sea washes in again.

The tough leathery fronds of the many different seaweeds can resist the drying effects of sun and wind. Even when the outer layer seems bone dry, if you lift the fronds you will find a dark, damp world inhabited by the sand-hoppers, shellfish and several kinds of crab. A rock pool might seem an unlikely spot to find hunters, but they are here. Look carefully and you might spot a predatory dog whelk steadily boring a hole in a mussel shell to get at the animal inside, or a starfish using its five powerful arms to drag open a **bivalve** shell. There are grazers, too. If you watch

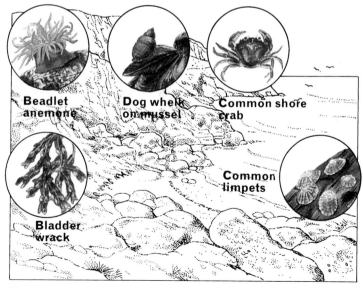

Beadlet anemone

Dog whelk on mussel

Common shore crab

Common limpets

Bladder wrack

some limpets with a viewer (page 22) when the tide has covered them, you will find them moving about, scraping algae off the rock. But each one returns to a 'home base' as the tide falls, clamping the edge of its shell into a tailor-made groove worn in the rock.

Sandy shores

On open stretches of sand, the only safe place at low tide is beneath the surface. Often the most obvious signs of life are the little mounds of coiled sand pushed up by burrowing worms, but look out also for funnel-shaped depressions which may reveal the presence of burrowing shellfish such as razor-shells, cockles and tellins, small sea urchins, or sand crabs.

Remember too that cliffs and beaches, salt marshes and especially the estuaries of large rivers, are marvellous places for watching wild birds. Resident gulls and terns wheel over the water, swooping to pick food from the surface or to dive after small fish. Eider ducks, redshanks, oyster-catchers and other specialist feeders prey on burrowing worms, crabs and shellfish. In winter, these birds are joined by thousands of turnstones and other migrating waders, pausing to feed as they travel north to breed in the Arctic regions.

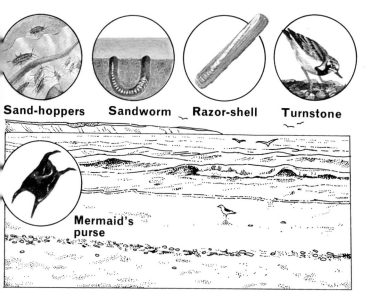

Sand-hoppers   **Sandworm**   **Razor-shell**   **Turnstone**

Mermaid's purse

3: Looking at Plants

Among all the strange and wonderful things in the world of nature it is a little odd to think of a simple leaf as one of the most remarkable and important things of all. Yet without the chemistry that takes place within green leaves there would be no animal life at all.

Every living creature depends on plant life. In a very simple **food chain**, a fox may eat a rabbit which in turn fed on grass. In a slightly longer chain, a snake might eat a frog whose last meal was a predatory spider that fed on the sap-sucking insects found on a flowering plant.

The secret ingredient

Green plants have the amazing ability to use the energy of the sun's light to make food. They use that energy to change carbon dioxide from the air, and water and a few dissolved nutrients from the ground, into the complex sugars and starches that are the building blocks of plant and animal life.

What makes the plants unique is **chlorophyll**, the chemical compound that gives them their characteristic green colour and which controls this life-giving chemical process of **photosynthesis** – literally, 'building with light'.

The world of plants

The plant kingdom is enormous, and includes a huge variety of shapes and structures. The very simplest forms, **bacteria**, have no chlorophyll, and belong somewhere on the borderline between primitive plants and animals. Higher up the scale come the **algae**, ranging in form from the green film that often covers the surface of a pond to the giant seaweeds that grow to almost 100 metres in length.

Then come the mosses and liverworts, simple plants that live in damp, poorly-lit places like forest undergrowth, and then the ferns – a huge group that includes tiny rock plants as well as the 10-metre-tall tree ferns of tropical jungles.

Finally there are the most advanced plants of all – the flowering plants. This huge group includes all the plants that produce flowers and seeds, from wild strawberries and marsh grasses to daffodils and the 110-metre-tall redwood trees of western North America.

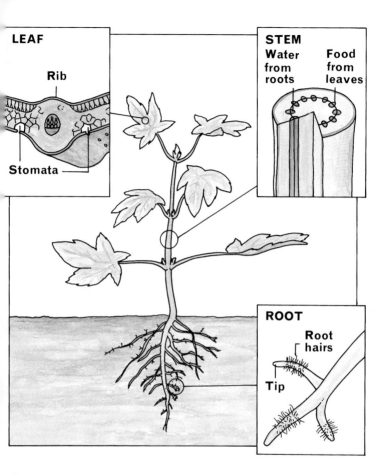

LEAF

Rib

Stomata

STEM
Water from roots

Food from leaves

ROOT

Root hairs

Tip

Plant structures

A typical plant, shown above, has three main parts. The roots anchor the plant in the ground and also suck up the water and dissolved nutrients it needs. Look closely with a hand-lens and you will see the fine root hairs that absorb water from the soil. The root tip is free of hairs and has a tough outer

The rigid stem holds the leaves up to the light. It has three main parts, which you can see with a lens on a freshly cut cross-section. (Use a very sharp knife or razor blade to avoid crushing it). Inside the tough outer skin is a layer called the **cortex**, and within this another called the **pith**. Growth takes place in a one-cell-thick layer – the **cambium** – separating the two. At this boundary you will see the fine tubes that carry food and water along the stem. Some stems are solid; others, like deadnettle and cow parsley, are hollow and these usually have strengthening ridges on the outside of the stem.

The leaf is where all the chemical activity takes place. Water and nutrients are carried to it from the stem, along the central rib and into the fine branching veins. Because the leaf is very thin, the carbon dioxide needed for photosynthesis can easily pass to all the cells after entering by the tiny pores (**stomata**) that cover the lower surface. The large surface area of the leaf exposes the greatest possible number of cells to the rays of the sun, and also helps the leaf to lose water vapour (see page 36).

Buds and twigs

The various scars you can see on a twig from a tree, such as the horse-chestnut twig shown below, are clues to the tree's annual cycle of growth.

As the tightly-packed bud opens (**1**) the protective outer

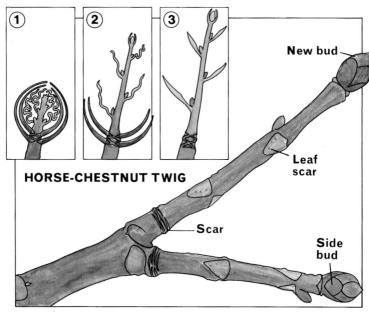

HORSE-CHESTNUT TWIG

New bud

Leaf scar

Scar

Side bud

scales bend back and the stem grows rapidly (2) as the new leaves unfold on either side. Finally the scales drop off, leaving scars that form a circle round the twig (3) while a new bud forms at the tip of the stem.

In autumn, the tubes carrying water to the leaf are sealed off. The leaf withers and falls, and a second type of scar is left on the twig. The different bark colours, bud shapes, twig forms and scar patterns of the common tree species make them well worth collecting.

Surviving the winter

Annual plants, which we look at on the next two pages, have no way of storing food. They survive winter only as seeds. The 'parent' plant always dies.

Perennial plants survive from year to year. They also produce seeds, but many can also reproduce from specialized food storage organs hidden away safely below the ground.

The plants illustrated below show three variations of this method. The daffodil has a bulb – a very short underground stem completely enclosed in fleshy leaves. Each year a new flower stem and new leaves grow from the bulb, nourished by food stored in the swollen bases of last year's leaves.

The potato plant stores its food reserves in a tuber – a greatly enlarged section of one of the many side-shoots growing from its stem below ground. The 'eyes' of a potato are buds, and each one can develop into a new shoot in the following year.

The third example, couch grass, has a rhizome – a long underground stem (*not* a root)

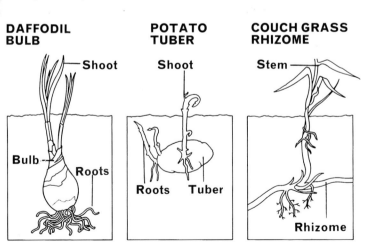

DAFFODIL BULB
Shoot
Bulb
Roots

POTATO TUBER
Shoot
Roots   Tuber

COUCH GRASS RHIZOME
Stem
Rhizome

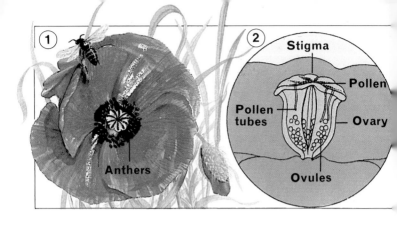

Figure labels:
1. Anthers
2. Stigma, Pollen, Pollen tubes, Ovary, Ovules

that is supplied with food by leaves above ground. As the rhizome gets longer it sends out side-branches, and also new leaves and stems to the surface.

Flowers and seeds

Producing the next generation of plants from seed is a much more complicated process, but it has two enormous advantages. First, by fertilizing the female **ovule** (egg) of one plant with male **pollen** from another, (see next column) the seed inherits characteristics of both 'parents'. This allows the species to evolve much more quickly, and with much greater variety, than is possible using the bulb or rhizome system. Secondly, putting the next generation plant in a tiny seed 'package' means that the seed can be carried far away from the parent plant, so the plant can spread to new areas.

How it works

Take a close look at a poppy, tulip or other common flower. Inside the ring of petals you can see numerous **stamens** holding up the pollen-covered **anthers**. In the middle is the **stigma**, the receptive female part, underneath which lies the **ovary** containing the ovules (eggs).

Pollen can be carried to the flower by the wind or running water, but the most common method uses insects as pollen carriers. In the example above, an insect, attracted by the flower's colour and scent, lands on the poppy (1). It's body is already dusted with pollen from other poppies. As it pushes into the flower to feed on the sweet nectar, pollen grains stick to the stigma. At once, each grain sends a pollen tube down into the ovary (2). As each one arrives it fertilizes an ovule. Their job done, the petals and

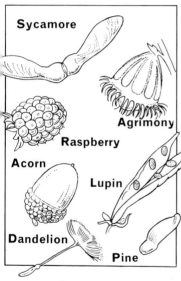

Sycamore

Agrimony

Raspberry

Acorn

Lupin

Dandelion

Pine

stamens die. The ovary (3) swells with the growing seeds until finally it bursts open, releasing the tiny seeds into the wind like a miniature pepper-pot (4). The details vary from one plant to another, but the basic method is the same. Use your hand-lens to examine as many different flowers as possible (including those of trees). Try to identify all the parts, and work out how the plant is pollinated.

Spreading the seed

Some plants have their seeds in attractive food-rich fruits and berries, which are eaten by birds. The bird digests the fruit, but the seed passes out in its droppings, quite unharmed, often several miles away.

Other plants, such as dandelion and sycamore, provide their seeds with feathers or vanes to help them drift away on the wind, and others, like agrimony, cover them with tiny hooks that catch in the coats of passing animals.

Collect as many different seed-types as you can, and classify them according to their methods of dispersal.

4: Plant Experiments

Using the humble french bean and simple pieces of equipment that are readily available in the home, you can carry out a whole range of experiments to investigate the structure and chemistry of plants.

Place a roll of blotting paper in a jam-jar as shown opposite. Trickle water into the jar until the paper is completely soaked and there is still a shallow layer of water in the bottom of the jar. Now slip some french beans down between the paper and the side of the jar. Alternatively, put some soil in the jar and slip the beans into it, close up against the glass.

For about three days the bean absorbs water and swells. (It could take longer in a very cool room or garden shed.) Then the seed-case splits and the root emerges (1). It grows downwards, quickly developing side branches and root hairs.

Once the root has a firm hold, the stem above it starts to grow – arching up in an elbow shape (2) until, in normal conditions, the elbow breaks through the soil. The stem straightens, pulling the young plant out of the ground and allowing its 'starter leaves' (called cotyledons) to open (3). These provide food for the plant but will drop off once

FRENCH BEAN PLANT

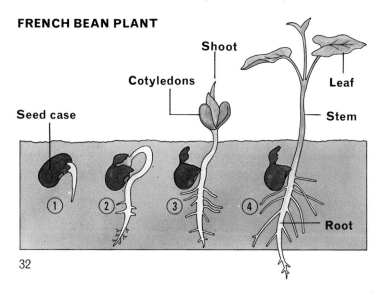

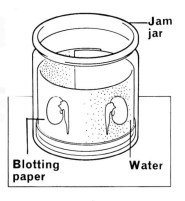

Jam jar

Blotting paper

Water

the first true leaves form (**4**). At this stage you can plant the bean outdoors if you wish.

For the experiments that follow you will need plants at various stages, so it is useful to start off a number of 'bean nurseries' at intervals of a few days.

Do plants 'feel' gravity?

The answer is yes. You can demonstrate that both roots and stems react to the force of gravity.

Take some beans with straight young roots and place them between pads of damp cotton wool in a shallow clear plastic box. The roots should stick out beyond the pads and the box should be positioned so that the roots are horizontal, as shown in the picture on the right.

Leave the box in a dark place for a couple of days (so that light plays no part in the test) and

you will find that the roots will all turn down – a reaction to the downwards pull of the earth's gravity.

You can perform a similar experiment with a more fully developed plant already transferred to a pot. Choose a plant with a straight stem about 8–10 cm tall. Place the pot on its side and cover it with a cardboard box (again so that light cannot affect the results). In a day or two the stem will have turned through a right-angle and will once more be growing vertically. Unlike the roots, the plant stem is 'programmed' to grow upwards – *against* the pull of the earth's gravity.

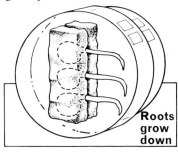

Roots grow down

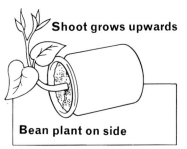

Shoot grows upwards

Bean plant on side

The plant's plumbing system

The fine tubes that run through the plant stem (page 27) are specialized into two types. One kind carries water from the roots to the leaves, while the other takes the food made in the leaves to other parts of the plant – for example to ripening fruit, new buds (page 28) or to underground storage organs (page 29).

The pressure in the root and stem system is quite high. After all, in a large tree the water on which the leaves depend may have to be raised 20 m or more above ground level.

A simple experiment demonstrates how water travels through the stem to the petals of a flower. Take a long-stalked flower – a white carnation is ideal – and split the stem. Place one section in plain water, the other in ink-stained water, as shown above. (Split three ways and use three colours if you like.) In a very short time the once-white flower will change colour, allowing you to see exactly where the coloured water is being taken.

What is osmosis?

Exactly how water is moved from one part of a plant to another is not fully understood, but it is probably mainly due to a process called osmosis. If one plant cell contains a strong

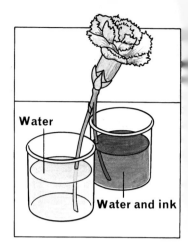

Water

Water and ink

chemical solution and another cell, next to it, contains a weak solution, water will move across into the cell containing the strong solution to try to dilute it. So, water in the soil is drawn through the thin cell walls of the root hairs and into the stronger solution of sap inside the cells.

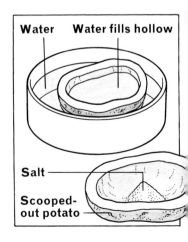

Water   Water fills hollow

Salt

Scooped-out potato

34

To show osmosis in action, cut a potato in half, hollow it out and place a spoonful of salt or sugar inside. Slice a patch of skin off the underside and stand the potato in a dish of water as shown opposite. The salt soon absorbs moisture from the cut surfaces of the potato, and so becomes a strong solution. Water is then drawn through the cells of the potato by osmosis in an attempt to dilute this solution. In a few hours the potato will fill and overflow. Try the experiment with an empty potato, and also with one that has been cooked first. Can you explain your results?

Do plants produce oxygen?

They do. In fact, without plant life our planet would never have developed its oxygen-rich atmosphere and there would have been no animal life.

Like all living cells, plant cells require oxygen. But oxygen is the side-product of photosynthesis, so the plants end up by producing far more than they use. Collect some pond weed and place it beneath a funnel in a deep container of water as illustrated here. A test-tube, completely filled with water, is placed over the funnel spout so that its open end is covered by the water in the container. The apparatus should then be left in a sunny place. As photosynthesis takes place, tiny bubbles of gas are released from the leaves to collect in the test tube. When enough gas has collected, it can be tested for oxygen. Light a taper, then blow it out to leave a brightly-glowing tip. Lift the test tube from the water and slip the taper inside. It will immediately burst into flame again. Oxygen is essential for burning, so this is a sure test that the gas in the tube is rich in oxygen.

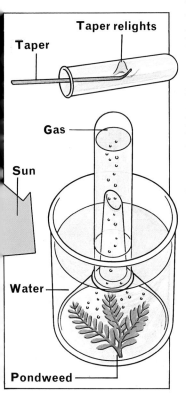

Taper relights

Taper

Gas

Sun

Water

Pondweed

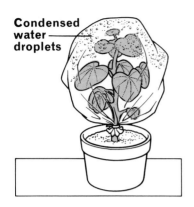

Condensed water droplets

Do plants 'perspire'?

In addition to releasing gases, the leaves of a growing plant give off water vapour in a process called **evapotranspiration**. The experiment shown above demonstrates how much may be given off by a small plant. Imagine then the millions of tons released into the atmosphere from a forest the size of the Amazon basin!

Simply place a clear polythene bag over the plant and tie it firmly round the base of the stem. In just an hour or two in the sun the inside of the bag will be misted over with water droplets.

Reaction to light

You can test the reaction of growing plants to light using one of your french bean shoots or a miniature 'forest' of grass or cress seedlings grown on wet cotton wool in a saucer.

Cut a slit in the side of a box, as shown below, and place it over the test plant with the lid on. In a day or two the plants will all lean towards the 'window' (**1**). Now leave the lid off for a couple of days and see what happens (**2**). Finally, replace the lid and allow the light to enter through a hole on the opposite side (**3**). (You can do this simply by turning the box round.) The plants will again start to lean towards the light.

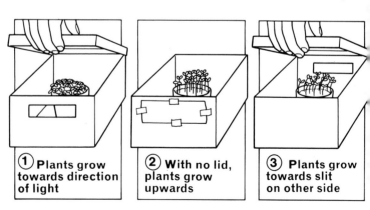

① Plants grow towards direction of light

② With no lid, plants grow upwards

③ Plants grow towards slit on other side

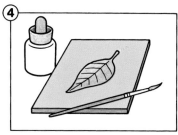

Exploring photosynthesis

The next few experiments test the conditions under which photosynthesis can take place. Since starch is a product of photosynthesis, we can use its presence or absence in a leaf to determine whether or not photosynthesis has been taking place.

At the start of each experiment, the test leaves have no starch in them. At the end we test for starch to see if any has been produced. If it has, we know that photosynthesis has taken place.

Leaves can be 'destarched' by putting the plant in a dark cupboard for two or three days. (Leaves on outdoor plants can be destarched by covering them with aluminium kitchen foil.)

Testing for starch

THIS TEST REQUIRES BOILING LIQUIDS. TAKE GREAT CARE, AND ALWAYS HANDLE THE LEAVES WITH TONGS OR TWEEZERS.

The test sequence is shown in the illustration above. First the test leaf is dipped in boiling water for half a minute to make it soft and to stop any further chemical changes taking place in it (1). Secondly, the leaf is boiled in methylated spirit (from a paint shop or hardware store) until all the chlorophyll has been removed and the leaf is white (2). THIS MUST BE DONE USING A WATER BATH. DO NOT HEAT THE METHS DIRECTLY. Thirdly, the leaf is again dipped in boiling water to soften it (the methylated spirit makes it brittle) and it is then laid on a ceramic tile (3). In the last stage, iodine solution (from a chemist's shop) is brushed over the leaf (4). Iodine reacts to the presence of starch by turning blue. So, a blue stain on the leaf is a clear indication that photosynthesis has taken place.

Test 1: Is chlorophyll essential for photosynthesis?

For this experiment you will need a **variegated** leaf – that is, one that has chlorophyll in some parts of the leaf but not in others. The attractive green and cream leaves of some kinds of ivy work well. So do the leaves of tradescantias and other decorative house-plants. First the leaf must be destarched. (Before starting the experiment, it is a good idea to remove one leaf and test it to ensure that the

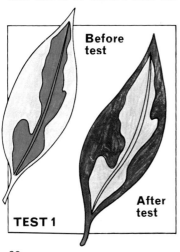

Before test

After test

TEST 1

plant *is* properly destarched. Then leave the plant in sunlight for a few hours, take another leaf, and carefully sketch the pattern of the green and non-green areas. Put the leaf through the starch test and make a second sketch, this time of the blue and brown stained areas. The blue areas will match the green areas of the original sketch, providing that starch has been produced only in those parts of the leaf that contained chlorophyll.

Test 2: Is light essential for photosynthesis?

First destarch your experiment plant, or selected leaves of a convenient plant in the garden.

From a strip of aluminium kitchen foil, cut a simple shape such as a star, a cross or one of your initials. Place the foil strip across the leaf as shown on the opposite page, wrapping it round the back of the leaf and making sure the edges are clipped together to stop light getting in anywhere.

Leave the plant exposed to the sun for about half a day, then remove the test leaf and put it through the starch test procedure. The blue stain will appear only on those parts of the leaf that were exposed to light. The parts of the leaf that were covered by the foil will have made no starch, even though they are well supplied with chlorophyll. This proves that light is essential.

Test 3: Is carbon dioxide essential for photosynthesis?

For this experiment, destarch a potted plant, water it well and then enclose it in a polythene bag, firmly tied round the rim of the pot as shown below. The pot should also contain a small dish containing soda lime (available from garden centres). This chemical absorbs carbon dioxide from the air inside the bag. NOTE: TREAT ALL CHEMICALS WITH THE GREATEST CARE. AVOID GETTING THE SODA LIME ON YOUR SKIN OR ANYWHERE NEAR YOUR MOUTH, AND WASH YOUR HANDS THOROUGHLY AFTER HANDLING THE DISH.

Leave the enclosed plant in a well-lit place for half a day, then remove a leaf and test it for starch production. With no carbon dioxide to use as a raw material, the leaf will have been unable to produce starch.

As a back-up experiment, set up another plant in exactly the same way but this time place some bicarbonate of soda dissolved in water in the dish. Instead of starving the plant of carbon dioxide, this chemical will make the air inside the bag very rich in the gas. Leave the plant in the sun for a few hours and test. Try out some variations on this experiment – for example, place a destarched plant in the CO_2-rich environment but with one leaf enclosed in a separate small bag, carefully sealed around the stem. What results would you expect to get?

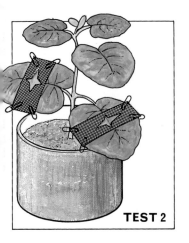

TEST 2

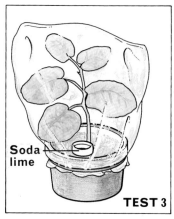

Soda lime

TEST 3

5: Studying Animals

In addition to looking at small animals out of doors, you can take some specimens home and study them at your leisure by keeping them in simple artificial environments. This allows you to follow their life-cycles and study their behaviour.

Ants are particularly good subjects to start with. They are easy to find and to look after, and most of the common species live in highly organized colonies which are fascinating to watch at close quarters.

Making an ant 'farm'

The drawings opposite show the main stages in making an ant 'farm' or formicarium. You will need a shallow wooden or plastic box, preferably about 30 x 50 cm, for the main mould. Alternatively you can make a tray from a sheet of hardboard with side walls of wood about 5 cm high. In the bottom, place a few small blocks of wood and one longer piece of wood near one end, as shown. Join the boxes together with thick 'ropes' of plasticine (1). Fill the tray with plaster of Paris and leave it to harden. When the plaster has set, turn out the cast (2). You will have a series of chambers linked by passageways. Clean off any rough edges and cover the cast with a sheet of glass or thick clear perspex (3). Make absolutely sure there are no gaps or you will have ants everywhere! Finally, make a light-proof cover of cloth or thick black paper (4). This should always be kept in place when you are not observing the ants.

Collecting your specimens

The easiest ant to collect is the small black garden ant, but you could also use the small orange ants whose grass-covered mounds are often found in meadows, or even the large red ants that are common under stones and rotten logs in most country areas.

The important thing when digging them up and putting them in a large plastic bag is to make sure you get a queen. She is easily recognized by her large size. If there are eggs and larvae in the nest, collect some of them too, but try not to take too much soil or leaf litter. Back at home, take the formicarium outdoors and tip the ants into the large chamber, replacing the lid immediately.

Care and maintenance

Keep the formicarium in a cool place, out of the sun. The ants will die if they get too hot and dry. Feed them on bits of fruit, seeds and raw meat placed in the large end chamber, and add a wad of cotton wool soaked in sugar-water. The ants will also make short work of any dead caterpillars or other insects you put in the feeding chamber. (This chamber need not be kept in darkness – see bottom illustration.)

If you lift the cover at intervals you will see workers moving the eggs and larvae between the chambers, looking after the queen, bringing food into the colony and carrying debris and dead bodies away to

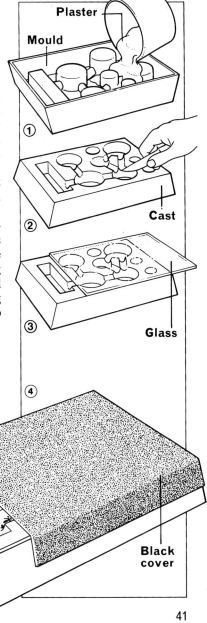

be dumped in the 'outside' chamber.

The non-reproductive female worker ants are wingless, but the males and young queens have wings. In the wild they swarm, flying off to start a new colony elsewhere. If you find your formicarium full of winged ants, release some of them in the garden, but make sure you keep a queen if you want your own colony to keep thriving.

Nature's gardeners

Earthworms are among the most useful and important of all small animals. Their constant burrowing ploughs the soil, breaking it down into fine particles and letting air and water pass freely to the roots of growing plants. They also fertilize the soil by dragging dead leaves down into the ground and by bringing mineral-rich soils up from deeper levels.

You can see for yourself just how efficient they are by building a simple wormery. All you need are two identical sheets of perspex and three lengths of wood about 2.5 cm thick. Make a wooden frame as shown opposite, then tape the transparent panels into place. Drill a couple of drain holes in the bottom section, and fit the wormery with a lid of wire gauze. The only other thing you need is a thick cloth to form a

light-proof cover. This should be kept in place except when you are observing the worms.

Soil-mixing equipment

Collect bags of soil of very different colours and textures – rich dark soil, sand, pale chalky soil, moorland peat soil and so on. Remove any stones and twigs, and then fill the wormery with alternating layers about 3 cm deep. Dampen each layer, but don't saturate it. Put a layer of gravel on the top and finally add a handful of dead leaves. Collect about a dozen worms from your garden, place them gently in the wormery, drape the cloth over the case – and watch what happens. If you inspect the wormery every few days you will soon find the soil layers becoming mixed together as the worms plough up and down through them. You will soon find worm 'casts' on the surface, and leaves will be pulled down as food.

How do worms breed?

Worms are hermaphrodite – that is, each worm has both male and female organs. But the worm can not fertilize its own eggs. To breed, the animals come together in pairs, lying parallel to each other while they exchange **sperm**.

When the worm is ready to lay its eggs, the characteristic

'saddle' in the middle of its body produces a detachable cocoon that slides along the worm's body, collecting a package of eggs as it goes. The cocoon slips over the end of the worm's body, the open ends close, and the eggs are held in the protective case until ready to hatch. If you examine the soil in the wormery you may find the egg case – or individual eggs about the size of rice grains.

Marsh worm

Common earthworm

Worm cast

Leaves pulled into burrow

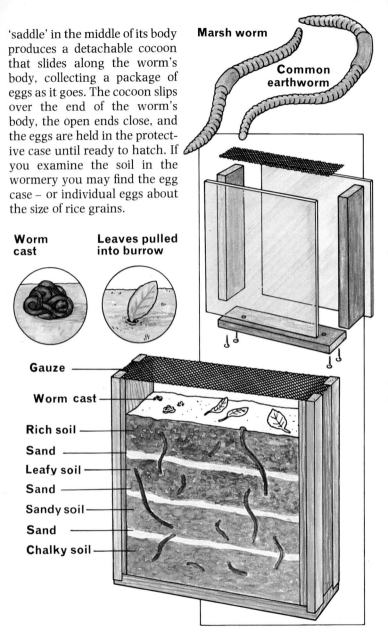

Gauze

Worm cast

Rich soil

Sand

Leafy soil

Sand

Sandy soil

Sand

Chalky soil

Investigating plant galls

On page 20 we mentioned some curious structures called galls, which grow on the leaves and twigs of the oak tree. The galls are made by the 'host' tree in response to the activities of a wide variety of insects. There are thousands of different kinds of galls (several hundred are found on oaks alone) and they can occur on leaves, leaf stems,

provides it with a food store and protective cocoon combined – without the insect doing any work at all.

Discovering what's inside

If you split a small oak gall such as a spangle gall you will find a small white grub inside. It is the larva of a tiny gall wasp. Other gall wasps are responsible for the much larger oak apple, and

Nail gall

Bedeguar gall

branches, trunks and even on the roots of plants.

Although they vary in size, shape and colour, the galls are all formed in much the same way. The female insect lays her eggs on the chosen tree, and flies off. The eggs hatch into larvae, and as they grow the plant produces a swollen mass of tissue around them. The gall does no harm to the plant, even though it is a reaction to physical damage. The benefit to the insect is obvious. The plant

the colourful bedeguar gall (also called the robin's pin-cushion) commonly found on wild roses growing in hedgerows. The curious pineapple gall, often found on spruce trees, is caused by an aphid; the bright red nail galls found on lime tree leaves are caused by mites, and the common leaf galls on willows are a response to sawfly grubs.

Hatching out galls can be a fascinating long-term project. Leaf galls should be collected in autumn when the galls are fully developed and the leaves are turning brown. You can delay collecting twig galls until all the leaves are gone.

Leaves with galls can be kept in an open plastic box with a muslin cover. They must be kept damp and cool until the insects emerge in the spring. Twigs bearing galls are best kept in water or damp peat in a

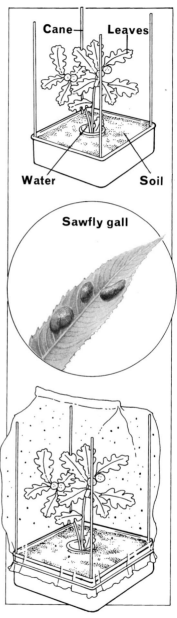

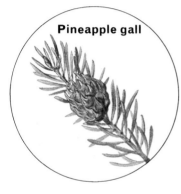

Pineapple gall

Sawfly gall

small jar inside a hatching cage as illustrated here. The framework is made of cane or stiff wire, and the cover from a clear plastic bag ventilated with pin holes.

Keep each type of gall in a spearate cage so you can see what kind of insect emerges from each type of gall. By referring to other, more specialized books, you will be able to follow the life-cycles of the different gall insects. Some of them are quite remarkable, and involve a two-year cycle with completely different galls in alternate years.

You will also find that very often the 'wrong' insect will emerge from a gall. This is because the galls are attacked by a host of parasitic insects. These lay their eggs in the young galls so that their own grubs can feed on the grubs of the gall insects.

Hatching butterflies and moths

Keeping butterfly or moth caterpillars until they hatch needs a little more care than hatching galls – but it offers a close-up view of one of the most spectacular transformations in the world of nature.

The swallowtail butterfly, for example, spends 8–10 days in its tiny pearly egg before hatching into a boldly-striped black-and-yellow caterpillar. After another 30 days the caterpillar spins a silken cocoon around its body, and remains in this **chrysalis** state for two weeks. Finally it emerges as an adult butterfly, with a life span of about 25–30 more days.

Make a hatching cage like the one in the picture opposite. You can collect specimens, either as eggs or as caterpillars, throughout the spring and summer. Each species will be found on the foliage of a particular favourite food plant. (A good field guide will tell you which species feed on which plants, and will also help you to avoid collecting any of the rarer species.) REMEMBER ALWAYS TO COLLECT SOME LEAVES OF THE FOOD PLANT ALONG WITH YOUR CATERPILLARS.

Some moths burrow into the ground to pupate, and if you recognize any of their caterpillars from your field-guide, you can collect and hatch them by providing a layer of soft moss, peat or compost in the cage bottom.

The transformation

At various times while in the cage the caterpillars will shed their skins. This is something most species do four or five times during the larval stage. It is necessary because of the very rapid growth of the caterpillar's body. After the last 'normal' moult, the caterpillars attach themselves to twigs by silk threads, or burrow into the ground. Then, in a final moult, the soft larval skin splits to expose the hard covering of the **pupa**. And there the animal remains, quite motionless, neither eating nor drinking, for anything between two weeks and several months. Caterpillars that pupate in spring usually hatch during the summer, while those that pupate in the summer months

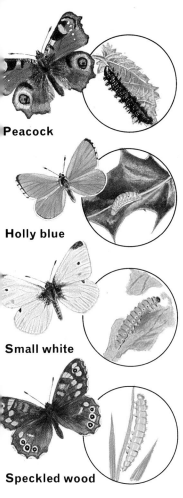

Peacock

Holly blue

Small white

Speckled wood

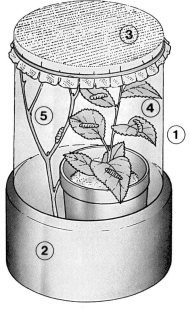

▲ To make a hatching cage:
Roll a sheet of clear acetate (**1**)
and fit it into the cut-off base of
a plastic bottle (**2**). Glue edges
together. Make a gauze cover
(**3**). Place fresh food plant
foliage in a small jar of water
each day (**4**). Add dry twigs for
caterpillars to attach to while
pupating (**5**).

usually lie dormant until the following spring. Eventually the great moment arrives. The case of the pupa splits, and out of it emerges a damp, crumpled, winged insect. Slowly its legs and body straighten and the delicate wing membranes stretch as blood fills the network of tiny veins. Finally, as they dry, the wings take on the shimmering colours that are characteristic of these insects.

After hatching, the insect should be released as soon as possible in its original habitat.

Raising frogs from tadpoles

Many animals, such as dogs, horses, rabbits and humans, produce young that are miniature versions of the adult animal. But in many groups of animals the individual goes through a series of dramatic changes before the recognizable adult form appears. Each of these changes is called a metamorphosis (from *meta* meaning change, and *morph* meaning shape).

We have just looked at the metamorphosis of moths and butterflies, and most other insects go through similar egg-grub-adult stages. Among land animals, the familiar frogs and toads of damp grassy habitats provide an opportunity to take a look at metamorphosis at close quarters. The animals are easy to collect and look after, and the whole process of change takes place over a period of about three months.

Where to start

As soon as the warm weather arrives in spring, frogs and toads emerge from their winter hibernation under rocks and logs or the tangled vegetation or hedge bottoms and ditches, and immediately head for ponds in order to breed. Try to collect your sample of frog spawn as soon as possible after breeding starts. You can find it almost anywhere in the pond, but the best place to look is among the water weeds around the edge. Half a jam-jar full is enough, as each clump of spawn may contain up to 4,000 eggs, each in its own little sphere of transparent jelly. You may also be lucky enough to find toad spawn. This is almost identical, but forms long strings rather than clumps.

Preparing the tank

An old fish tank makes an ideal container, but any watertight plastic box or tank will do. In the later stages the young frogs will need to leave the water, so you could save time by setting up the tank as shown opposite, with a number of fairly large stones that rise above the water level.

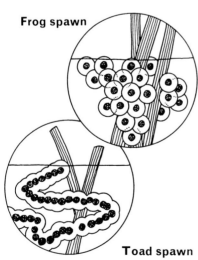

Frog spawn

Toad spawn

The metamorphosis

Place the spawn in the tank (DON'T MIX FROG AND TOAD SPAWN). Start keeping a project notebook with a record of the date and the temperature of the water, and from then on try to take the temperature, and make your notes and sketches, at the same time each day. In a few days the tiny dot inside each egg capsule will change into a comma shape, which will eventually wriggle free of the jelly and cling to a frond of weed. This tiny tadpole has feathery outer gills for breathing. In a few days these disappear as the internal gills take over. Observe the tadpoles feeding. At this stage thay are plant-feeders, scraping algae off the surface of the pond weed. At about seven weeks the back legs start to develop, and 2–3 weeks later the front legs appear.

During this period the tadpoles' diet changes. They start to eat more and more animal food so give them some 'ants' eggs' fish food (available from pet shops) and some tiny scraps of raw meat.

Soon after the front legs develop, the tail starts to shorten and the tadpole starts rising to the surface to breathe air. At this stage it *must* have a dry-land area in the tank, because at about 12 weeks the frogs leave the water and spend most of their time on land. As soon as they start spending a lot of time out of the water, the young frogs should be released close to the original pond. It just isn't possible to keep them supplied with their natural food.

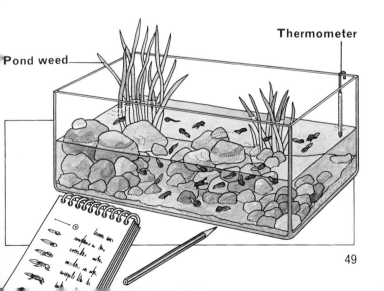

Thermometer

Pond weed

6: Garden Projects

At the start of this book we said that the world of wildlife begins right outside your own door. And so it does, for even the smallest garden is teeming with life, with opportunities for a huge variety of projects.

Spiders, it has to be said, are not the most popular of small animals, especially when they find their way indoors. But they certainly do not deserve their bad reputation. Viewed under a magnifying glass they are quite spectacular creatures, and in their own natural habitats are among the most interesting subjects you could ever choose to observe.

One of the most common species is the garden cross spider – so called because of the prominent white markings on its back. This is the spider whose large spiral webs are suspended between bushes and flower stems all over the garden. But look at the webs very closely. You will find that one species of orb-web spider always leaves an open sector in its spiral web.

Watch how carefully a spider looks after its web. If you drop a small piece of grass or a small feather on the web, the spider will immediately set about wrapping it in silk thread before

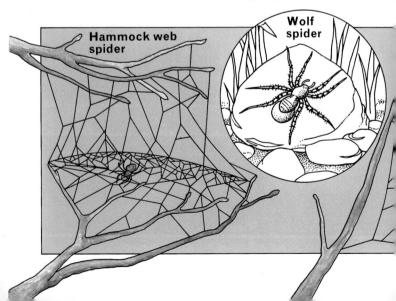

Hammock web spider

Wolf spider

snipping it free and throwing it clear of the web. Try making a bigger version of the butterfly cage on page 47 and put a spider inside, with an open arrangement of twigs. Then you can study just how it goes about constructing a web.

Other spiders to look for include the wolf spider, a lone hunter that takes its prey in a running attack instead of using a web. The female carries her eggs in a silk-wrapped bundle beneath her body. The black-and-white striped zebra spider is another 'loner' that stalks its prey on open ground, walls and fences, and attacks by pouncing.

If you look inside flowers you might find very small spiders that scurry with a sideways movement. These are crab spiders, lurking in wait for the flying insects that visit the flower for its nectar.

The tops of bushes and privet hedges are often covered in a haze of very fine horizontal webs. Look closely. The small spiders that make them can be seen hanging upside down underneath the webs, ready to strike upwards at insects that land on them. Many of these webs have fine 'trip-wire' threads above them to alert the spiders to approaching victims. Finally, here are two unusual webs to look for. The wall spider lives in a crevice in a wall or the bark of a tree, lining its hole with silk and running long trip wires out in all directions around the entrance. When an insect hits one of these, the spider rushes out to attack.

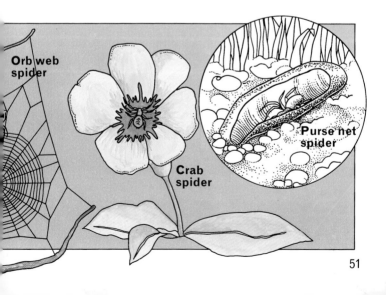

Orb web spider

Crab spider

Purse net spider

The purse net spider makes a silk cocoon like the finger of a glove, concealed in the surface soil or leaf litter. When an insect alights, the spider stabs it through the 'purse' with its poisoned fangs, and drags it down inside the cocoon.

Welcoming bees and wasps

We tend to think of bees as **colonial** insects that live in natural or man-made hives and swarm at regular intervals, but this is really true only for the honey-bee. The bumblebee also lives in a colony, but one which is much smaller, less organized, and not designed to last through the winter. Apart from these two, most of the 250 bee species in Britain are solitary bees. Their habits are extremely interesting and by encouraging them into the garden you will also gain the benefit of some of nature's most efficient plant pollinators.

The same is true of wasps. The swarming common wasp is unpopular with most people, but there are also many useful and attractive solitary wasps, many of which prey on caterpillars, flies, aphids and other garden pests which they use as food for their larvae.

Providing accommodation

Digger wasps and mining bees lay their eggs in burrows in the ground, or in holes in old woodwork, decaying logs, or masonry. The main difference is that the wasps stock their egg chambers with insect food for their grubs, while the bees stock theirs with honey, neatly packaged in papery cells, rolled-up leaves or even tiny pots of clay.

You can attract these insects by offering ready-made living quarters. A bundle of large drinking straws can be fixed to a house or shed wall, for example. One end of each straw should be blocked, but vary this so that each end of the bundle has some open ends. Another method is to make holes of various sizes – say 4 mm up to 10 mm – in a log and put it in a quiet part of the garden.

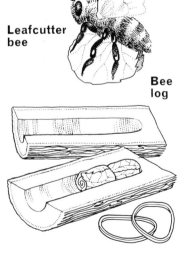

Leafcutter bee

Bee log

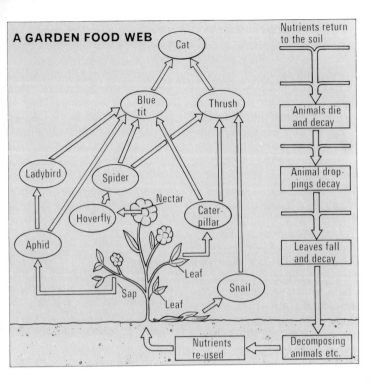

A GARDEN FOOD WEB

Cat

Blue tit

Thrush

Ladybird

Spider

Nectar

Hoverfly

Cater-pillar

Aphid

Leaf

Sap

Snail

Leaf

Nutrients return to the soil

Animals die and decay

Animal drop-pings decay

Leaves fall and decay

Nutrients re-used

Decomposing animals etc.

Perhaps the best method of all is to use split bamboo canes or pieces of wood drilled first and then split, as shown on page 52. Then, once the bee has finished laying, you can look inside the chamber every few days and watch the larvae developing. This is a marvellous way to admire the work of the leaf-cutter bee, whose egg-cells are made from almost circular pieces cut from the leaves of plants (often roses) and then rolled into neat tubes with leaf plugs at each end.

A garden food web

By this stage you will have become quite skilled at working out the life-styles of many common garden and country-side animals. The next step is to work out just how the various plants and animals relate to each other. The best way to do this is to construct a **food web** diagram along the lines of the one shown above. On this, you can show who eats what, how energy is passed along the chain from one animal to the next, and how the food supplies in the system are recycled again and again.

You can make diagrams like this for any unit – a corner of the garden, a single rose bush, a section of marsh or beach, or even an entire forest. The basic 'rules' remain the same whatever the size of the unit. You can use the arrows in either of two ways. Choose one, but try not to mix them up. One system shows 'who eats who', so the arrows start with the unit's highest predator and form a chain. The other system shows the movement of food energy *up* the chain, starting with the plants, which make food, using the sun's energy, and ending up with the top predators.

Remember that in a small unit you will have just a few simple chains, perhaps only one. In a large unit there are many chains, and many of these will be interlinked, forming what naturalists call a 'food web'.

Follow that snail
On pages 24–25 we looked at the feeding habits and movements of the common limpet. This experiment looks at one of the limpet's land-based relatives, the garden snail.

If you look under large stones, upturned plant-pots and large leaves close to the earth, you will find snails resting

during the day. You can mark their shells with a dab of paint and then, when evening falls, use a red-filtered lamp to watch them browsing on their favourite plant foods. Make a sketch plan of their feeding territory and plot their movements. How far do they travel? Which plants do they prefer? By using numbers rather than just dots, you will be able to check which snails return to a particular 'home base' and which,

if any, take up residence in a new shelter at dawn. Keep a record of their movements over several days. Are there any regular patterns of behaviour?

Estimating populations
Zoologists and botanists use a number of statistical methods in their research. Some are very complex, but this technique is quite simple, and is ideal for estimating populations of small

creatures like wood lice. It is called the 'capture-mark-recapture' method.

Choose a study area with plenty of wood lice and measure its total area. Suppose you had an area 3 m × 4 m (12 square metres) between a shed and a compost heap. Use pegs and string (or a quadrat if you have one) to mark a 1 m-square test area. Go out at night and capture every wood louse in the square. Mark each one with a dab of paint (on the underside to avoid making it a sitting target for predators) then let them all go – again inside the test area.

On the following night, capture every wood louse inside the test square once again. Count the total and also note the number of marked lice. Now multiply the number of lice caught and marked on the first night by the number caught on the second night. Divide the answer by the number of *marked* lice found on the second night. Your answer will give you an estimate of the population within the test square. (For greater accuracy, repeat the test with other one-metre squares and take an average.)

To estimate the total population of the study area, multiply this 'one-square' population by the number of square metres in your area (in this case, multiply by 12).

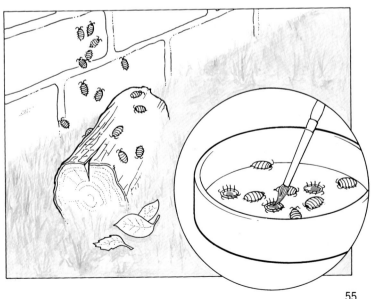

7: Watching Birdlife

Of all our native animals, by far the most familiar, noisy and colourful are the birds. And there is no better place to start bird-watching than your own garden or local park. An added attraction is that of all nature study hobbies, bird-watching is the one with the most clubs, societies and magazines, and has enthusiasts from nine years old to ninety in every part of the world.

To make a start, simply find a comfortable spot in the garden where you will be partly hidden but will have a good all-round view. Keep still and quiet and the birds will carry on with their normal activities. You are almost certain to see at least half a dozen species – and probably a lot more in the spring and summer when the birds are busy nesting, mating and bringing up their young.

One of the most pleasant surprises is to discover just how attractive many of the most common birds are when they are seen at close quarters. The cock sparrow in spring has beautiful bold markings, and a tough, cheeky attitude to life. The starling is often accused of being a noisy, dirty nuisance,

especially in towns. But look again. On a sunny day its dark glossy plumage shimmers with flecks of every colour imaginable. Among the small, colourful birds, you might see the acrobatic members of the tit family, or the striking chaffinch, while the splendid pink, black and white bullfinch might be making himself rather less popular by stripping buds off

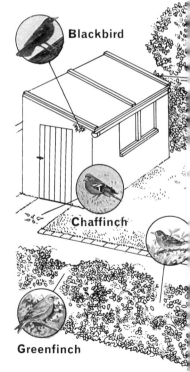

Blackbird

Chaffinch

Greenfinch

the apple tree. If you are lucky, the garden might have a re-sident robin – one of the great characters of the bird world. He is often quite tame around people, but defends his territory with fierce aggression against any other robin who tries to muscle in!

Among the larger garden birds are the blackbird and thrush, both of which have delightful songs, and you are likely to see woodpigeons and collared doves too, especially if there is woodland nearby.

Hidden away in hedges, or scurrying over the ground searching for food, you might see a dunnock (also called the hedge sparrow) or the tiny wren, whose loud and cheerful voice always seems far too big for such a small bird.

Investigating territories

In the spring you can very easily demonstrate just how fiercely a robin will defend his territory. Take an old sock and roll it into a ball, roughly the size of a bird. Then pin a patch of red cloth or paper to the sock to represent the red breast of a

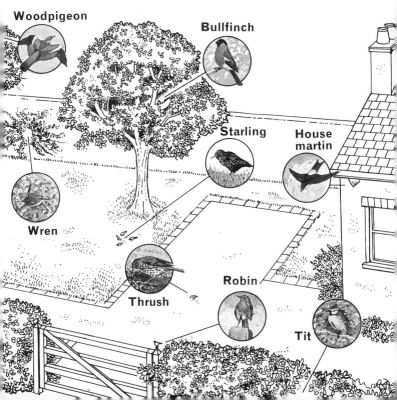

Woodpigeon
Bullfinch
Starling
House martin
Wren
Thrush
Robin
Tit

Robin

Dummy robin

robin. Stand the dummy robin on a fence-post or on a wall in another robin's territory – and stand back. The resident robin will go through his 'threat' display and will even attack the 'intruder' in an attempt to drive it away. DO NOT LEAVE THE DUMMY THERE FOR MORE THAN A FEW MINUTES. IF LEFT TOO LONG IT COULD MAKE THE RIGHTFUL RESIDENT LEAVE THE TERRITORY.

You can also use the dummy (again with great care) to work out the size of a resident robin's territory. Place the dummy well beyond the territory, then move it gradually inwards. Stop as soon as the resident robin becomes agitated. Plot that position on a sketch map of the area. Try again somewhere else, and again plot the point at which the resident bird gets annoyed. Each point you plot

represents a point on the edge of the bird's territory. Take great care with the experiment. Remember that when you leave one bird's territory you may step straight into that of another.

Encouraging bird visitors

In winter, when natural food is scarce, you can attract birds to your garden by offering them food. But don't start winter feeding unless you intend to continue right through, as the birds may come to depend on you.

There are a number of pre-packed foodstuffs for garden birds but bits of bacon rind, meat fat, unsalted nuts, raisins and other fruits, moistened bread, seeds of all kinds, oatmeal and broken biscuits will all be eaten. In thick snow, help the insect-feeders too by scraping some parts of the garden clear. In very severe weather you could even put out some mealworms or other grubs obtained from an angling bait shop. Finally, but very importantly, birds need water. Keep a dish in the garden – and remember to break the ice on frosty mornings.

You can also take an all-year-round approach by stocking your garden with plants that are useful to birds, either directly, by bearing seeds or

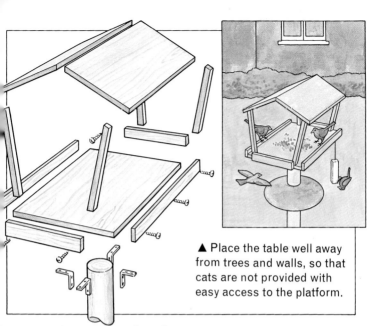

▲ Place the table well away from trees and walls, so that cats are not provided with easy access to the platform.

nutritious berries, or indirectly by supporting the insects that many birds feed on.

Bird tables and feeders

The drawing above illustrates one very popular style of bird table. Size is not critical, but to attract a reasonable number of birds the platform should be at least 30 cm × 35 cm. It is very simple to make, using low-cost wood screwed together or fixed in place with small nails and wood-glue. To make it last, the wood should be treated with a preservative. Important points to note are the gaps in the side rails at the corners, to allow rain-water to drain away and also to make cleaning easier, and the funnel-shaped guard on the support post to prevent cats or squirrels climbing up to the platform.

As well as enabling you to watch the birds, your table can be the basis for an experiment. Place small dishes of food on the

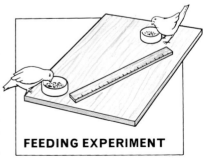

FEEDING EXPERIMENT

table with a ruler alongside, as shown on page 59. Watch the birds and note whether they feed quietly or start fighting. Move the dishes nearer and observe again. Try this with birds of different species. You will find they have a widely differing tolerance of the closeness of other feeding birds, both of their own species and others.

For the acrobatic blue tits and great tits, thread peanuts (in their shells) onto pieces of string and hang them up where you can watch. In winter, make a mixture of suet, fat, cake crumbs and nuts. Press the mixture into foil baking cups and string them up too. Keep a careful note of which birds try to use the hanging feeders. It is surprising how many different species will try when the going gets tough – even though this may not be their normal method of feeding.

Who eats what?

You can get a general idea of a bird's main food from the shape of its bill. Seed and nut eaters have short, thick, powerful bills for crushing. Waders have long slender bills for probing. Insect feeders usually have sharp, thin bills; meat eaters have hooked bills for tearing; ducks have broad bills for grazing and dabbling, and so it goes on. The bills of our garden birds are a mixture of insect eater, seed-eater and 'general-purpose' types.

But within these groups, individual species have their preferences, and this is something you can investigate in your own garden. Set out small dishes containing a variety of different foods, and keep notes of which birds take food from each dish. This kind of experiment should be repeated at the same time of day on several consecutive days: the more records you have, the more reliable your conclusions will be. It is also best to move the dishes around each day. You

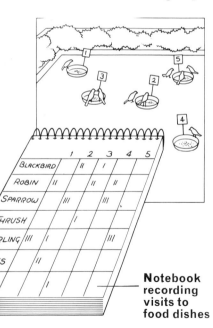

Notebook recording visits to food dishes

60

want to be sure that a bird is choosing cake crumbs, for example, and not choosing the dish farthest from the house.

Nest boxes and nest sites

Nothing can beat the pleasure and satisfaction of watching a pair of birds nest and produce a family in your garden, so try to encourage them by providing good nesting sites.

Try to preserve good natural nesting sites like old trees, dense shrubbery and ivy-covered walls, but add a few new sites – nesting boxes, an old kettle or large jug hidden in a hedge or bush (spout downwards to drain off water), a pile of bricks and plant pots in a corner, with plenty of gaps and spaces for small birds, perhaps (with your parents agreement!) even an access hole cut under the eaves of a garden shed to let thrushes and blackbirds in.

The drawings show three common nest box types. Standard hole-fronted boxes are ideal for tits and tree sparrows if the hole is no larger than 28 mm diameter. Holes up to 50 mm will let in larger birds, but the opportunist sparrow will often get there first. The exact size of the box is not important, but it should be about 15 cm wide, 12 cm front to back, with side-pieces sloping from about 25 cm to 20 cm. The

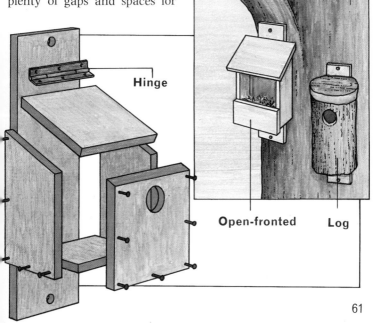

Hinge

Open-fronted   Log

lid should be hinged, and it is best to drill drain-holes in the base to keep the box dry.

Open-fronted boxes, similar in size, are popular with robins and spotted flycatchers, and larger versions can be used to attract birds like owls and jackdaws. Attractive and natural-looking nest-boxes can also be made from hollowed-out logs.

Take care in placing the box. It should be sheltered from wind and rain and should be out of direct sunshine. Fix it to a tree or fence post, or to the wall of a shed or the house, but choose a spot as difficult as possible for cats to get at.

The first sign of use will be the parent birds carrying nesting materials into the box. You can look inside every few days, but wait until the birds are away. When you find eggs in the nest, leave the birds in peace until the eggs have hatched. That stage will be obvious. Quite apart from the cheeping of the young birds, the parent birds will be seen working overtime carrying food to satisfy their offspring's enormous appetites. If you keep a careful and regular watch, you will eventually see the young birds peeping out of the hole. After that, with a bit of luck, you might even see the baby birds making their first attempts to fly.

Getting out and about

One of the great pleasures of bird-watching is that you can do it anywhere. Once you have developed the basic skills of observing and taking notes, and are beginning to recognize a reasonable number of birds, the time has come to try your hand at field-work.

By far the best way to learn more is to join a local bird-watching club. That way you will be able to go out with more

experienced bird watchers. In addition to the outdoor equipment and clothing described earlier, you will need a good field-guide and a pair of binoculars. These need not be very expensive, but go for the best you can afford – and try them out before buying. For all-round use buy 8 × 30 or 8 × 40 binoculars, and if possible choose a lightweight model. Remember that you will be carrying them and using them all day.

An observation hide

To get really close to birds so that you can observe them for a reasonably long time without disturbing them, you need a hide. They are simple to make and require no expensive parts.

You will need four strong stakes about 2 m long, and four more about 1 m long. These are lashed together with string or cord as illustrated below to make a rigid frame. The cover is made from canvas or other tough material (an old tent is ideal) and should be daubed with uneven patches of brown and green paint for a camouflage effect.

Access is through a slit in the back, covered by a flap or closed with blanket pins when in use. The viewing holes are vertical slits cut in the canvas. You can make several, at different heights, but keep them pinned shut when not in use as birds are sensitive to the slightest movement.

A hide is an ideal place from which to take photographs, as you can set up your camera on a tripod inside, with the lens peeping out of one of the slits. Once inside, you are free to move, make notes, consult your identification guides and even have your lunch – all without disturbing your target birds. But do remember to keep very quiet. Ring-top drinks cans and noisy lunch wrappings can be disastrous if you're very close.

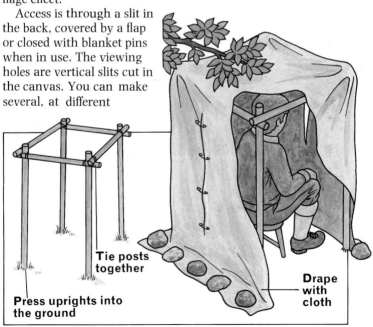

Tie posts together

Press uprights into the ground

Drape with cloth

8: Making a Collection

Many of the specimens you collect on nature study outings can be used to make displays of various kinds. Others can be used for further experiments and investigations which you can follow up in the evenings or when the weather is bad.

Just where and how you display your collection will depend on the amount of space you have. This need not be very large. With a little imagination and planning you can create work space, storage space and an impressive display area out of one corner of a small bedroom. If you are lucky enough to have a spare room, an empty loft or a dry cellar that can be used as a hobbies room, so much the better. The extra space is useful, and it does allow you the freedom to leave a project part-finished and return to it later.

Science and safety

The best scientific research is invariably done slowly, methodically and with strict rules for safety. While you are working, scalpels, modelling knives, needles and probes should be kept in a shallow dish, or placed with the sharp end down in a stable jar or tin with a cork or rubber pad in the bottom. After use they should be put away securely – especially if there are young children in the house.

Strict care must also be taken with any chemicals that are used. If possible, store them outdoors in a garage or garden shed, and always make sure the top is on properly, as many substances (e.g. the preserving

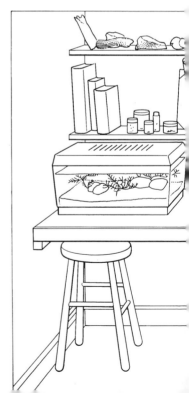

solution mentioned earlier on) give off dangerous vapours. For this reason, double-check specimen tubes and jars containing preservatives.

Flexible work-space

If you have room, a sturdy work-bench or table placed against a wall with good natural light will give you the best possible conditions. With careful planning of bookshelves and storage space, you can use the table as a nature study laboratory and as a place to do your homework and other projects.

If space is limited, your parents may be able to build you a narrower work-bench fixed to the wall with heavy-duty hinges so that the work surface can be swung down flat against the wall when not in use. The top can be supported in use by chains running to hooks fixed to the wall, or by fold-away legs.

Storage and display

Collect cardboard and plastic boxes and jars of all shapes and sizes. Larger ones can be used to store fossils, pieces of bark and

other robust specimens. A storage container for small specimens such as shells, bird pellets and beetles can be made from matchboxes glued together in stacks to make miniature chests of drawers. Split-pin paper fasteners make suitably sized drawer handles.

Shallow wooden boxes such as cigar boxes are ideal for displaying beetle and butterfly specimens. Line the box with cotton wool, arrange the specimens inside, then glue a sheet of perspex or clear acetate over the top in place of the lid.

Feathers, dried grasses, photographs and other small items can be displayed on a pinboard, or by slipping them beneath strips of dressmaking tape pinned to the board in a diamond pattern as shown in the illustration on page 65.

Grasses and flowers
Large plant specimens with a fairly low moisture content, like reeds, grasses, teazles, poppy heads and the attractive plant 'honesty' with its paper-thin seed-pods, are best preserved by natural drying. Simply hang them up in a bunch, heads downwards, in a well ventilated place until completely dry.

Wild flowers are best preserved by pressing them between sheets of absorbent paper in a flower press, as illustrated

below. Arrange the flowers on a sheet of blotting paper, place another sheet on top, then add a sheet of corrugated cardboard. This sequence can be repeated several times, then the stacked sheets are clamped firmly between the wooden boards of the press and left in a warm dry place for several weeks. Alternatively, the stack can be pressed under a pile of heavy books.

Once the flowers are dry you can arrange them on sheets of thick white paper, holding

them in position with thin strips of adhesive paper. The sheets can be stored in a large loose-leaf album or mounted for wall display.

Bark rubbings and casts

You can build up a useful and attractive collection of tree bark patterns by taking bark rubbings. Fix a sheet of thick drawing paper to the tree as shown above, then rub over the entire surface with a thick wax crayon or piece of chalk.

Write the name of the tree on the back of the rubbing, along with a brief description of the height and thickness of the tree, the time of year, and a note of which side of the tree you worked on. (The texture on the side exposed to wind may differ from that on the sheltered side.) The rubbings can be kept in a folder made of stiff cardboard, or they can be mounted on card and hung on the wall.

An alternative method of recording bark patterns is to press a sheet of plasticine or modelling clay against the bark, then peel it off very carefully. Carry this three-dimensional impression home and use it, as described on page 69, to make a plaster cast of the tree's surface. You could then paint the cast in the tree's natural colours.

Mounting spider webs

Lightly spray both sides of the web with commercial artist's aerosol glue, taking care not to hold the can too close. Then lightly dust the chosen 'front' surface with talcum powder to make it white.

Take a sheet of matt black paper or card and bring this up behind the web. The trick is to touch all parts of the web at the same time so that its shape is not disturbed. As soon as the web has stuck to the card, cut it free from its support threads and take the web indoors. Taking great care not to damage the web or mark the black card, place the mounted specimen between two sheets of perspex for permanent display.

Analysing bird pellets

Some bird pellets separate quite easily using the 'dry' method – that is, teasing the bones and matted hair apart with tweezers and a couple of thick needles mounted in corks.

For more stubborn pellets, use the 'wet' method. Place the pellet in water in a jar and swirl it round gently. Skim off any feathers and hairs that float to the top then pour off the water, add fresh water, and continue swirling until the pellet softens.

Carefully pour off the water and tip the solid remains into a shallow dish or tray. In a large owl pellet you may find hundreds of small bones and bone fragments – the remains of the shrews, mice and voles that make up the bulk of the owl's diet. Sort the bones into piles – skulls, jaw fragments, ribs, limbs etc – and try to identify what species they belonged to.

ANALYSING PELLETS

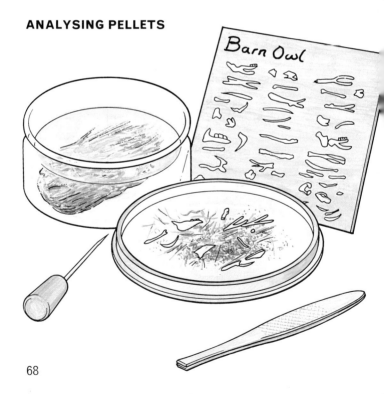

Barn Owl

You will probably need some extra books from the local library for this. There are also several field guides which will help you to identify which bird produced a particular pellet.

Finally, wash the fragments in disinfectant, let them dry then mount them on a display card labelled with the name of the bird, the date and place of collection, and notes on the pellet's contents.

Making plaster casts

The technique of making plaster casts is very simple and can be used to make a permanent record of a wide variety of natural history subjects. For example, as well as the footprints illustrated here, you can make casts of tree bark impressions (see page 67), fossils (using exactly the same method), twigs and leaves, bones, shells and so on. With most of these subjects you need to make an impression first, in plasticine or clay, to act as a mould for the plaster. Footprints form natural moulds, so no intermediate stage is necessary.

To make the cast, first place a strip of card held by a paper-clip around the footprint (1). Mix your plaster of Paris to a smooth paste and pour it into the mould (2). Use a stick or spoon to work the plaster into every corner.

When the plaster has set, lift the cast free (3), remove the paper strip and brush off any soil or grass sticking to the cast.

Use a modelling knife or scraper to clean up any rough areas of plaster, then mount the cast, either painted or sealed with clear varnish.

69

9: Threats to Nature

A good all-round knowledge of natural history is a great source of pleasure and satisfaction. Once 'hooked', most people retain that interest for the rest of their lives. But this understanding of how the natural world works is also very important for its long-term survival. By understanding how natural systems work, we can see and understand the dangers they face from human activity – and hopefully do something about them.

One of the biggest problems all over the world is the destruction of natural habitats. The area of forest destroyed every year is at least equal to the size of England. Some scientists believe it may be twice as much.

▲ Above left: Seabird covered in oil from sea pollution; Above right: Forest clearance for crop plantation in Thailand; page 71, left: Industrial air pollution; right: agriculture in Scotland.

Cutting down trees for their wood is one reason, but most forest clearance is to make more land available for agriculture. And in the dry lands that lie south of the Sahara Desert, from Chad right across to Ethiopia, sparse natural scrublands are reduced to desert as wood is cut for fuel, and goats and cattle eat every scrap of vegetation they can find, just in order to survive.

The people of the world's poorer countries cannot be held to blame for this destruction.

They have little choice. But in the developed countries of America, Europe, Northern Asia and Australasia there *is* a choice. These areas have abundant food, yet marshlands are drained, hedgerows and woods are ripped out to make bigger 'more efficient' fields, more and more chemicals are poured onto the land every year, and the air and the oceans are being polluted with the waste materials of our industries.

Nobody pretends that it would be possible to support the

world's population without causing any damage to the environment. There are simply too many people for that to be possible. But the damage can be drastically reduced, and in some countries it is being reduced – due mainly to the constant pressure put on governments by the various conservation organizations.

The pesticide threat

The problem with many of the chemicals used to kill insect pests is that they do not decay into harmless substances once their job is done. They remain, and what is worse, they are stored in the body tissues of animals that eat them in their food. So, in the food chain illustrated here, snails might take in chemicals sprayed onto a crop (1). The thrush eats the snails – and stores in its body all the chemicals from all the snails it eats (2). A predator at the top of the chain will collect all the chemicals stored in the bodies of the animals it kills (3). What might start off as a 'harmless' dose when it is first sprayed on the land can quickly become fatal higher up the food chain.

Looking for signs

Certain plants and animals are particularly sensitive to air and water pollution and can provide a guide to local pollution levels.

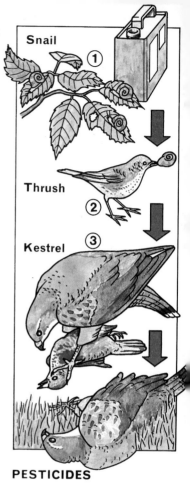

PESTICIDES

The delicately branched grey and green lichens commonly found on trees out in the country are very sensitive to the sulphur dioxide in polluted air. They soon disappear as you approach a town. The round patches of orange lichen can survive moderate levels of pol-

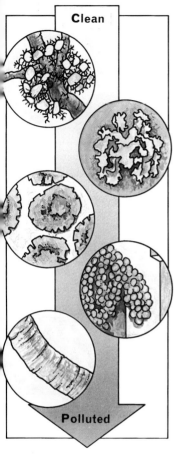

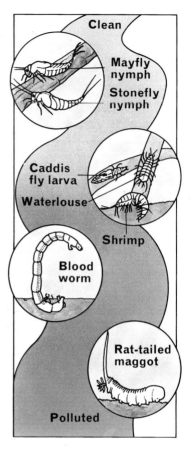

AIR POLLUTION

lution, but where the air is very bad, only a thin film of green algae will be found on trees and stones.

In rivers and streams the various insect larvae are good indicators. Mayfly and stonefly nymphs are indicators of clean water. They cannot tolerate

WATER POLLUTION

polluted conditions. Caddis larvae can withstand a little pollution, and bloodworms quite a lot, but if a sample of river water contains no larvae other than rat-tailed maggots (the larvae of a drone-fly) it is a sure sign that the water is heavily polluted.

10: Getting Involved

Conservation is for everybody. It is something that begins with you: with the way you think about the world around you and the way you think the world should be in the future. Just by getting interested in nature study you have begun to get involved in conservation.

Big national and international organizations are needed to tackle international problems – like pollution of the atmosphere, the trade in rare and endangered animals, and the destruction of important habitats. But conservation is also something that can be put into practice in your own neighbourhood.

Local projects

Many conservation projects involve quite a lot of heavy work, so try to get a group together – preferably with a few keen adults as well. Some of them will have very useful technical knowledge because of their jobs.

You could form your group with friends at school, or at a youth centre or sports club. The important thing is to have enough people to spread the work out – and also have fun at the same time.

Choosing a project

One important type of project is the 'Operation Clean-up' kind. The group might take on a small patch of woodland, a disused railway siding, a pond or a run-down piece of common land. Sites like these are often littered with rubbish. They look a mess and are also very dangerous. Cleaned up and replanted with extra shrubs, bushes and flowers, they can be turned into small parks, and give pleasure to the whole community.

Don't be shy of asking for help. Make a detailed plan of the area – as it is now, and as it will be when it is finished – and take this to the local council. They might be prepared to give a small grant towards the cost of tools, new plants or materials. Try local businesses too. They might sponsor the project with cash, materials, tools or help with transportation.

Another popular kind of project is to develop a patch of waste ground as a nature reserve. Again, you will have to clean the place up, but this time your replanting schemes should include a wide variety of plants that provide food for butterflies and moths, from nettles, honeysuckle and rosebay willow herb to shrubs and trees like buddleia, alder and buckthorn.

A good range of bushes and trees, especially those bearing nuts, berries and other fruits, will attract birds at all times of the year. If natural nest sites are in short supply, add a variety of nest boxes.

If you are starting with a completely cleared site, leave one area of earth bare as an experimental plot. Inspect this area at regular intervals and take notes of the plants that colonize it. You will find that the mixture of plants will alter with time.

A third kind of project includes elements of the two already described, but with an added bonus. You can use part of your space as a produce garden, to grow vegetables, and fruits such as raspberries. It is the best possible way to find out about organic farming – that is, growing things without using chemicals – and as well as enjoying the fruits of your own work you might be able to sell some of the produce.

▼ Tree planting by conservation volunteers.

Glossary

Algae Primitive plants that live in water or in damp places. They vary in size from the green powder on tree trunks to giant seaweeds nearly 100 metres long.

Annual A plant that grows from a seed, flowers and produces more seeds, and then dies – all in a single year.

Anthers The pollen-producing lobes at the upper end of the stamen – the male part of the flower.

Bacteria Microscopic single-celled plants. Most are harmless but some cause disease. Bacteria play an important part in breaking down animal and plant remains in natural cycles.

Bivalve A sea- or freshwater mollusc with a hinged double shell, e.g. an oyster or clam.

Botanist A scientist who makes a special study of plant life.

Cambium The thin layer of cells in a plant stem where growth takes place. In a tree the cambium lies between the bark and the trunk wood.

Carnivore An animal that lives on flesh or other animal matter e.g. stoats, eagles, spiders, frogs, sharks. There are also a few carnivorous plants, such at the Venus flytrap and the common sundew.

Chlorophyll The green chemical in plants that enables them to harness sunlight and use it to fuel chemical changes.

Chrysalis The pupa of a moth or butterfly.

Colonial Living in very large groups, or colonies. Colonial animals include ants and bees, rabbits, seals and many birds, especially seabirds such as gulls, terns and penguins.

Cortex The part of a plant stem between the outer skin and the cambium.

Evapotranspiration The name given to the process by which water is evaporated into the air as water vapour from the leaves of growing plants.

Food chain The natural links between animals and their food. For example, owl eats shrew, which eats earthworm, which eats leaves.

Food web The interlinking of many different food chains

due to many animals having a wide choice of food.

Gall A swelling or lump of plant tissue formed on a leaf, stem or root as a reaction to the egg-laying activities of a wide range of insects.

Habitat The natural living place of a plant or animal.

Herbivore A plant eater.

Leaf-litter The layer of dead leaves, twigs and other plant debris covering the ground, especially in woodland.

Ovary The tough case in the centre of a flower that contains and protects the ovules. In many plants (e.g. apple) the ovary swells into a fruit after the flower has been fertilized.

Ovule The part of the flower which, when fertilized, develops into a seed.

Pellets Rounded or oval 'packages' of animal hair, fish scales, bones and the hard parts of insects, regurgitated (coughed up) by various birds.

Perennial A plant that is able to survive the winter and so continue living year after year. (Compare with annual).

Photosynthesis The chemical process by which water and carbon dioxide are turned into carbohydrates in the leaves of green plants.

Pith The cells filling the central part of a plant stem.

Pollen The male sex cells of the flowering plants, produced by the anthers and carried to other flowers by the wind or by insects.

Pupa The stage in the insect life-cycle between larva and adult. In this stage the insect is usually contained in a cocoon while it completely reorganizes the structure of its body.

Recycling The repeated use of raw materials. In nature this is achieved by dead animal and plant material decomposing so that the chemical building blocks return to the soil for use again by growing plants.

Sperm The male sex cells in animals: their function is to fertilize the egg of the female.

Stamen The male part of the flower, consisting of the thin stalk (the filament) and the pollen-bearing anthers.

Stigma The receptive part of the female flower: the part the male pollen sticks to at the start of fertilization.

Stomata The minute holes or pores in the surface of a leaf, which allow gases to enter and enable the plant to lose excess water.

Variegated Leaves having two or more colours – often in irregular patterns.

Zoologists Scientists with a special interest in animal life.

Index

Acknowledgements

Photographs: Andrew Cleave/Nature Photographers
p5; C. Gomershall/Nature Photographers p70 (left);
Michael Chinery p70 (right); Dr Baer/Zefa p71 (left); C.
Mylne/Nature Photographers p71 (right); British Trust
for Conservation Volunteers, South West p74

Artwork: Eagle Artists; Hayward & Martin